Contents

Introduction

It would be a rare primary teacher who said that they had time to spare; but even in the busiest day there may be a few minutes left after the work has been done and everything is packed away. This is the perfect opportunity to carry out a quick science demonstration that will fire children's imaginations.

The activities in this book are intended for teacher demonstration, but, wherever possible and safe, children should be involved in the practical aspects of the activity. Learning for all children will be enhanced by the opportunity to participate, even if their experience is vicarious. However, when allowing children to participate in activities involving food be aware of allergies or other dietary conditions such as diabetes.

It is not essential that children come up with the 'correct' scientific explanations, many of which lie outside the KS2 programme of study. Rather, the main point of all these demonstrations is to get them discussing ideas with each other and the teacher, as well as using reasoned arguments to predict and explain the outcome of the activities.

With this in mind, it is important not to give away the right answer too soon as this will stop the discussion. Many teachers may even choose not to give the scientific explanation at all, preferring to leave their pupils curious. This may stimulate many pupils to continue the discussions outside the classroom or to undertake some research for themselves.

Finally, most *Six Minute Science* can be done with very little preparation, but it is advisable to try the activities out yourself before showing them to the class so that you are comfortable with what to do and what to expect, ensuring the best results.

2

How to use Six Minute Science

Each activity is organised under the following headings:

What you need: Tells you exactly what you need for the activity.

What you do: Tells you what to prepare and what to do in the classroom, and sometimes suggests what to ask (in italics).

What happens: Describes the results you should get.

Why it happens: Explains, in simple scientific terms, why you should get those results.

By the way: Gives extra information, including extension activities and safety issues where necessary.

This sign indicates that the activity must be carried out by an adult or under adult supervision due to the use of heat, sharp objects, etc.

Curriculum links: The references at the bottom of each activity provide a link to the National Curriculum for England and the QCA Schemes of Work. In addition to the references given, these activities all relate to the KS2 Sc1 Scientific Enquiry section. There are also links to the National Guidelines for Environmental Studies in Scotland, a key for which is provided on p.48.

We wish you many an enjoyable and thought provoking 'Six Minutes'!

The right beak for the job

Demonstrate that birds have different-shaped beaks depending on what they eat.

In the classroom

What you need

Some chocolate beans, three cups, two cocktail sticks, two lollipop sticks, a plastic cup with the top rim cut off so it opens and closes like a mouth and a stopwatch or clock.

What you do

Spread some of the chocolate beans out on your table.
Give three children a cup each.
Say that they can keep as many sweets as they can pick up in one minute, but that they must use only the tool you give them and only use one hand for the tool.
Now give your volunteers their 'beaks'. Give one child two cocktail sticks, another two lollipop sticks and a third the plastic cup.
What kinds of foods would be easiest to eat with each of the beaks?

What happens

It is likely that the plastic cup will be the best scoop, but you may be surprised!

Background Information

Why it happens

Different birds have different-shaped beaks and they use them accordingly to eat insects, seeds, nuts, fruit, etc. The activity shows that one beak is better suited to a particular task than the others. Animals and plants survive in a wide range of living conditions, and so each species develop methods for dealing with their specific environment. We call this *adaptation*.

By the way

What kind of beak would be good for feeding from water? For feeding on insects in bark? For cracking open seeds?
It was his observations of the beak shapes of Galapagos finches that first led Charles Darwin to think about how animals adapt to their environment – in this case, to eating different sorts of food.

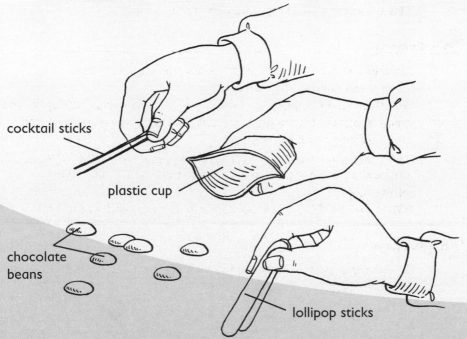

cocktail sticks

plastic cup

chocolate beans

lollipop sticks

Curriculum links

KS2 Sc2 5b. QCA SoW 6A Interdependence and adaptation
Envtl St/Science/LT&PL/VCF/Level E/Target 3/ILTTE/Level D/Target 2

floating fish

Make a potato-fish float in between salty water and coloured fresh water.

In the classroom

What you need

Two jugs of water (one with salt added and stirred until no more dissolves and the other with a drop of food colouring added), a potato, a knife, an empty plastic pop bottle, a spoon and an aquarium.

What you do

Make a fish by cutting a potato slice 'body'.
Cut some triangular plastic fins from the bottle and push them into the sides of the potato slice.
Then pour the salty water into the aquarium.
Slowly add the coloured fresh water by pouring it over the back of a spoon like cream.
Put the fish carefully on the surface of the water and watch what happens.

What happens

The two kinds of water separate to form two layers, the fresh layer over the salty layer. The fish floats between the two layers of water!

Background Information

Why it happens

This has to do with the relative densities of the two liquids, salty water and fresh water. A simple answer is that a potato will float in very salty water but not in fresh water. Floating happens when there is a balance between the downward pull of gravity and the upthrust of the water.

By the way

Ensure that enough salt has been added or the water won't separate into two layers.

Colouring the fresh water helps children see the two kinds of water clearly, and you will of course show them the salt. However, it may also suggest that potatoes sink in coloured water! Somebody will ask you to 'stir it up' – what happens then? Some children will know that it is easier to float in salt water than in fresh water – it is almost impossible to sink in very salty water, like that found in the Dead Sea.

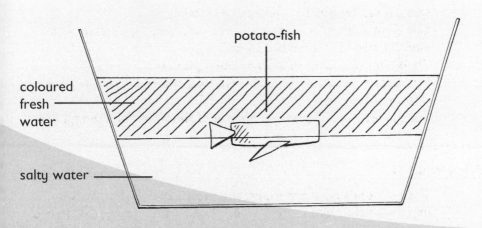

potato-fish

coloured fresh water

salty water

Curriculum links

KS2 Sc3 2a,d 3e. QCA SoW 6C More about dissolving
Envtl St/Science/E&S/CM/Level C/Target 3/E&F/FTE/Level A/Target 1

Separating different liquids

Show how different liquids separate according to their different densities

In the classroom

What you need

A tray, a tall transparent cylindrical container with a lid, some golden syrup, some cooking oil and some water.

What you do

Put the cylindrical container in the tray to catch any spills.
Pour some golden syrup into it.
Watch how long it takes to form a level surface.
Pour in some oil.
Pour in some water and put the lid on.
Shake the container so that everything is mixed up, then leave it and watch what happens.

What happens

The three liquids form three layers. The syrup lies at the bottom, the oil sits on the top and the water forms a band in the middle. When shaken and left, the liquids will separate out into these three component layers again (although the layers will mix together slowly if left for several days).

Background Information

Why it happens

The syrup is the most dense liquid and water, surprisingly, is denser than oil. This means that a cupful of water is heavier than an equal cupful of oil. The liquids separate out in order of density with the least dense at the top.

By the way

Talk to children about how the oil and the vinegar separate out in French dressing.
Discuss other combinations of liquids and encourage children to suggest their relative densities and what layers they would form.

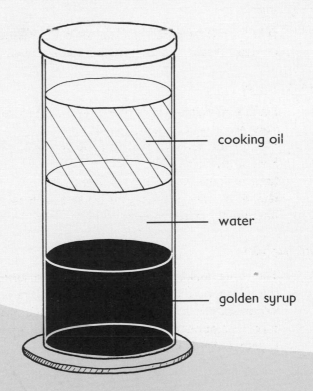

cooking oil

water

golden syrup

Curriculum links

KS2 Sc3 3e. QCA SoW 4D Solids, liquids and how they can be separated
Envtl St/Science/E&S/ME/Level B/Target 2/Level E/Target 1/CM/Level C/Target 1

King Kong's hand

Inflate a rubber glove using carbon dioxide from the reaction between bicarbonate of soda and vinegar.

In the classroom

What you need

Some vinegar, an empty milk bottle, some bicarbonate of soda, a rubber glove and some elastic bands.

What you do

In advance, pour a little vinegar into the bottom of the milk bottle and a little bicarbonate of soda into the fingers of the rubber glove. Letting the rubber glove hang by the side of the bottle, fit the wrist of the glove over the top of the bottle and make it airtight with elastic bands.

When you are ready for the demonstration, lift the glove and shake the bicarbonate of soda into the vinegar.

Ask the children to watch what happens.

What happens

The mixture fizzes and the glove starts to inflate. Eventually, it stands upright like a waving hand.

Background Information

Why it happens

Vinegar and bicarbonate of soda react to make carbon dioxide gas. This tries to escape out of the bottle but goes into the glove and in the process, inflates the hand.

By the way

Drawing knuckles on the gloves adds to the fun.
You can inflate a glove much more slowly with yeast and warm water.

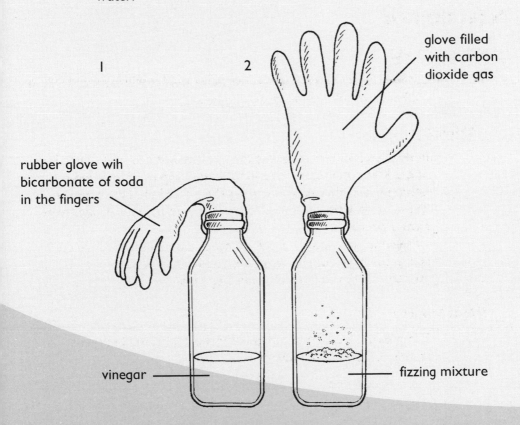

1

2

glove filled with carbon dioxide gas

rubber glove wih bicarbonate of soda in the fingers

vinegar

fizzing mixture

Curriculum links

KS2 Sc3 2a,f. QCA SoW 6D Reversible and irreversible changes
Envtl St/Science/E&S/CM/Level E/Target 1

Cleaning Copper Coins

Clean a copper coin using the mild acids in tomato ketchup.

In the Classroom

What you need

Some dirty copper coins, paper towels and some ketchup.

What you do

Look at the copper coins.
Explain to the class that they are filthy and that you would really like them clean.
Show them the ketchup.
Polish the coins with a paper towel and some tomato ketchup.
How could the ketchup clean the coins?

What happens

The coins come out bright and shiny! Rinse them and pass them round.

Background Information

Why it happens

Oxides form naturally on the surface of metals as they react with the oxygen in the air, making them look dull and dirty. Tomato ketchup is an acidic food and the acid removes the oxides from the surface of the coin.

By the way

Water speeds up the reaction between oxygen and metals, which is why iron and steel rust faster when wet.

Remind the children that their stomach is acidic too – they will have tasted that if they have ever been sick. Incidentally, if they are unlucky enough to be sick, they should clean their teeth. The stomach acids will do their tooth enamel no good at all!

 Make sure children don't eat the ketchup.

Curriculum links

KS2 Sc3 2a,f. QCA SoW 6D Reversible and irreversible changes
Envtl St/Science/E&S/CM/Level E/Target 1

Marble run

A row of marbles act like a Newton's cradle, transferring energy from one end to the other on impact.

In the classroom

What you need

Some marbles and a toy car track (or similar grooved track), or you can use a length of plastic curtain rail.

What you do

Put a row of marbles in the track, making sure they are all touching.
Hold one marble in your hand.
What will happen if I roll the marble into the row?
Roll the marble towards the row of marbles – hard!

What happens

The row of marbles stays where it is but the last marble flies off the end.

Background Information

Why it happens

The energy you gave the first marble was transferred through all the marbles in the row to the very last one, which moved. All the marbles in the middle are trapped by their neighbours. They can transmit the energy but they can't move. The end marble, however, is free to move in one direction, which is why it flies off!

By the way

Newton's cradle and other executive toys use this trick. Children could try rolling marbles on a flat surface, making them collide, and see what happens each time.

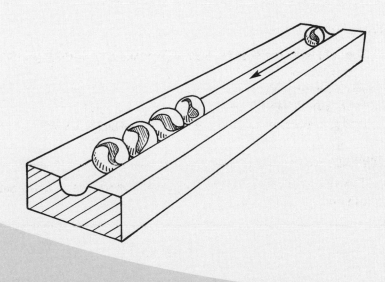

Curriculum links

KS2 Sc4 2d,e. QCA SoW 6E Forces in action
Envtl St/Science/E&F/FTE/Level E/Target 1

Defying gravity

Stack up a pile of books so that they hang improbably over the edge of a table.

In the classroom

What you need

Six books of the same size.

What you do

Start to stack the books at the edge of a table.
Line the first book with the edge of the table, the next book should overhang the table by about 2 cm, the next book by 2 cm more, and so on.
Keep adding the books.

What happens

You end up with the books looking like a flight of stairs off the table edge, yet they don't fall.

Background Information

Why it happens

Although the stack leans off the table, the place where the weight of the books is concentrated – called the *centre of gravity* – remains on the table. So don't be too ambitious. Looking at the stack from the side, the bulk of the books should still be on the table edge.

By the way

You may need to adjust the books slightly as you go along to ensure that the weight of the books remains on the table. Moving the last book out a shade may cause the pile to fall!

Curriculum links

KS2 Sc4 2b,e. QCA SoW 6E Forces in action
Envtl St/Science/E&F/FTE/Level D/Target 2/Level E/Target 1

Bouncing balls

Children will be surprised by what happens when you bounce two balls on top of one another.

In the classroom

What you need

A football and a tennis ball.

What you do

Hold out the football.
Hold the tennis ball vertically above the football.
Drop them both together.
Ask the children to watch closely and describe what happens.
Do it again.

What happens

The football hits the ground, bounces up and hits the descending tennis ball. The tennis ball leaps high into the air.

Background Information

Why it happens

When the football hits the ground, the energy of its fall is transferred by its bounce into lifting it again. This large amount of energy is transferred to the smaller tennis ball and it is far more than the tennis ball would have received if bounced alone. Therefore, the tennis ball leaps high into the air.

By the way

When a collision happens between a large object and a small one, energy is exchanged or swapped, between the two. So, if a bus and car collide the car is likely to get more damaged because a bigger amount of energy is transferred to it from the bus than the other way around.

Curriculum links

KS2 Sc4 2b,d,e. QCA SoW 6E Forces in action
Envtl St/Science/E&F/FTE/Level D/Target 2/CTE/Level E/Target 1

Floating ball

Show the children how to make a ball float using a fast stream of air.

In the Classroom

What you need

A hairdryer with a 'cool' setting and a table tennis ball.

What you do

Switch on the hair dryer to 'cool'.
Hold it so that the air blast is straight upwards.
Show the children the table tennis ball.
Then gently put the table tennis ball into the air stream.

What happens

The ball is suspended in the stream of air. Even if you gently angle the hair dryer one way or the other, the ball stays in the stream.

Background Information

Why it happens

The jet of fast moving air produces an area of low pressure. The surrounding air has a slightly higher pressure, so it pushes inward, trapping the ball in the stream.

By the way

Tilt the stream too much and the ball will fall out of it!

 You must use a hair dryer that is approved for safe use in schools. Do not use a hair dryer or other mains appliance near water. Do not do the activity if you have concerns about children doing the activity at home without proper precautions.

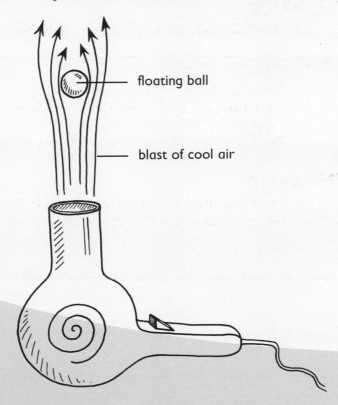

floating ball

blast of cool air

Curriculum links

KS2 Sc4 2d,e. QCA SoW 6E Forces in action
Envtl St/Science/E&S/ME/Level E/Target 1

Can you balance a cup?

Balance a cup or mug on your finger using a couple of table knives to lower the centre of gravity.

In the Classroom

What you need

A teacup or mug, two blunt table knives and a roll of stiff paper.

What you do

Hold up the mug.
How can I balance this mug on my fingertip?
Attempt to balance the mug from the centre of its base but catch it when it falls!
Push two knives through the handle, one from either side, so that their handles hang down.
Jam them in place with a small roll of stiff paper.
Balance the mug on your finger and ask for an explanation.

What happens

The knife handles hang down on either side of your finger and the mug balances.

Background Information

Why it happens

An object's *centre of gravity* is the point where the entire mass of
the object may be regarded as being concentrated. Adding the
knives lowers the centre of gravity of the mug below your
fingertip. It is now easy to balance on your outstretched finger.

By the way

You can even have the mug filled with water without it losing its
balance.
Compare this with other balancing tricks – the long-tailed parrot
toy, for example, and the long pole carried by tightrope walkers.

Take care in case the mug does fall and smash.

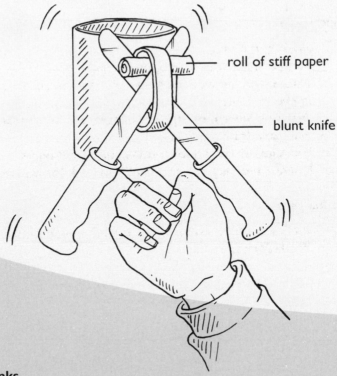

roll of stiff paper

blunt knife

Curriculum links

KS2 Sc4 2b,d,e. QCA SoW 6E Forces in action
Envtl St/Science/E&F/FTE/Level D/Target 2

Fascinating forces

Apply your knowledge of forces to perform a simple magic trick.

In the classroom

What you need

A paper cup, a paper loop made from a 30 cm paper strip glued at the ends and a coin.

What you do

What force pulls us all downwards?
Put a paper cup on the table.
Place the paper loop upright on the rim of the cup.
Balance the coin on top of the loop.
Challenge the children to knock the loop out of the way so that the coin falls into the cup. They are likely to fail.
You then try it by flicking the loop from the inside, and succeed – every time!

What happens

The children are all likely to hit the loop on the outside causing the coin to leap into the air, but you strike the loop from the inside, which pulls it out of the way, allowing the coin to drop into the cup.

Background Information

Why it happens

If you hit the loop on the outside, you change its shape so that the top of the loop pops up and the coin leaps into the air. If you hit it on the inside, however, you flatten the loop and drag it off the cup. The coin then drops into the cup.

This is an application of *inertia*. Newton was the first to record the fact that things stay exactly where they are, or keep moving in exactly the same way, unless an external force is applied. Your technique removes the upward force (support) the loop gave to the coin. Instead, left without support as you whip the loop away, the coin responds to the one force that acts on everything – gravity.

By the way

Talk about inertia in daily life, e.g. standing without support in a bus as it starts to move – you lose your balance.

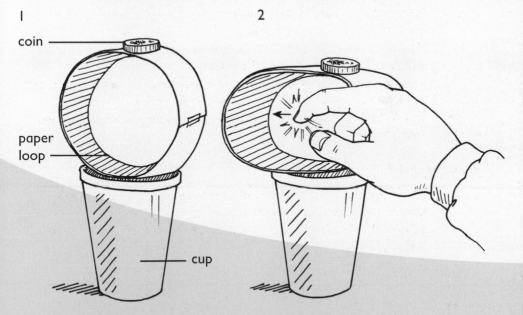

1

coin

paper
loop

cup

2

Curriculum links

KS2 Sc4 2b,e. QCA SoW 6E Forces in action
Envtl St/Science/E&F/FTE/Level E/Target 1/Level D/Target 2

Rolling uphill

Everything rolls downhill – doesn't it? This illusion suggests that things can roll uphill too!

In the Classroom

What you need

Two 1 m rulers, a pile of books, an elastic band and a roller made from two plastic funnels taped together at the mouth.

What you do

Hold the bottom end of the two rulers together with an elastic band.
Place the rulers side by side so that they form a ramp using the pile of books.
Produce the funnel roller and rest it on the ruler 'track' near the top end.
Slowly pull the rulers apart at the top end and watch the roller closely.

What happens

As you pull the rulers apart, the roller appears to begin to move towards you, up the ramp.

Background Information

Why it happens

As the gap between the rules widens, the funnels drop slightly and spin forwards. This forward movement makes it look as if the funnels are climbing upwards when in fact they are slipping downwards.

By the way

Now try this activity with a ball. What happens?

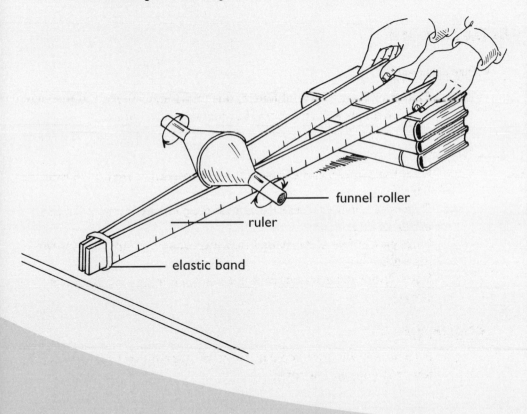

funnel roller

ruler

elastic band

Curriculum links

KS2 Sc4 2b,e. QCA SoW 6E Forces in action
Envtl St/Science/E&F/FTE/Level E/Target 1/Level D/Target 2

Streams of water

Merge separate streams of water into one, thanks to surface tension.

In the Classroom

What you need

A cardboard milk container or drink carton that you have washed out and rinsed very thoroughly, masking tape and some water. Make six small holes in a row on one side of the carton, about I cm apart and close to the bottom of the box.

What you do

Show the children the box and tape over the holes.
Fill the box with water.
Hold it over the sink and strip off the tape.
Pinch the streams together and observe what happens.
Release the streams and observe what happens.
Repeat the pinching and releasing.

What happens

At first, six streams of water pour from the holes, but when you pinch them together with your fingers they become one stream. You can split them apart again by removing your fingers, and then join them again.

Background Information

Why it happens

Water particles are attracted to each other. It is this attraction between identical particles (cohesion) that produces the 'skin' on water – called *surface tension*. This force of attraction is strong enough to keep the streams together. By making all the streams one with your fingers, you combine them in a single skin.

By the way

It is this 'skin' on water that makes it so hard to dissolve powder paint. A drop of washing up liquid added to the water makes the job much easier as the detergent breaks down the skin.

That's also why it is important to rinse every trace of detergent from the milk container or drink carton before carrying out this activity.

water

Curriculum links

KS2 Sc3 1e. QCA SoW 6E Forces in action
Envtl St/Science/E&S/ME/Level E/Target 1

Can rocks float?

Pumice is a volcanic rock that challenges children's knowledge about the properties of rocks and stones.

In the Classroom

What you need

Pieces of pumice stone and a bowl of water.

What you do

What makes a rock a rock?
As well as talking about hardness, weight and so on, ask the children what happens to rocks in water.
Once you have established that rocks sink, produce a pumice stone.
Invite the class to examine it. It is a stone, all right, but one from a volcano.
How is it different from other stones?
Now put it in the water.

What happens

The pumice stone floats.

Background Information

Why it happens

This volcanic rock is a kind of hardened foam. When it was molten, it was filled with boiling gas so when it cooled, air pockets 'set' inside the rock. These gas bubbles in the rock make it light. In fact, it is less dense than water and so it floats.

By the way

There are other such exceptions to familiar rules. Ebony, for example, is a wood so dense that it sinks in water.

pumice stone

water

Curriculum links

KS2 Sc3 1a Sc4 2b,e. QCA SoW 6E Forces in action
Envtl St/Science/E&S/ME/Level E/Target 1

unit 6E Does water have a force?

Water jets from a milk carton cause it to spin round on the end of a string.

In the classroom

What you need

A clean, empty milk carton and some thin string.

What you do

Make a small hole in the lower left-hand corner of each side of the milk carton, and cut the top off.

Tie a length of thin string to the top, making sure that the carton hangs straight.

Fill the container over the sink using a fast tap, so that it fills faster than it empties.

Hold it up – full – by the string and watch what happens.

What happens

Jets spout from the holes and the box spins round and round in a clockwise direction.

Background Information

Why it happens

The jets of water evoke an equal and opposite force to their direction of flow. The force pushes against the carton corners and the carton spins.

By the way

This is an illustration of Newton's third law: every action has an equal and opposite reaction. Another example is the recoil, or jerking back of a gun when a bullet is fired from it.
What would happen if the holes were in the lower right-hand corners?
The box would spin in the opposite direction.
What would happen if the holes were in the middle of the sides?
The box would spout water but it would stay still.

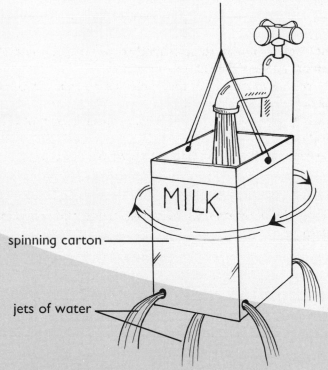

spinning carton

MILK

jets of water

Curriculum links

KS2 Sc4 2d,e. QCA SoW 6E Forces in action
Envtl St/Science/E&F/FTE/Level B/Target 1/Level E/Target 1

Returning roller

With some preparation a closed can can be made to roll away from you, stop, and then start rolling back again.

In the classroom

What you need

An empty can with a fitted lid, like a coffee can or custard powder tin, and with two holes in the lid and two in the base. You also need a length of thin elastic made from elastic bands knotted together and a weight.

What you do

In advance, thread the elastic through the holes in each end of the can and tie the ends together.
Hang the weight from the centre of the band, inside the can, and put the lid on.
In class, place the can on its side on a table and push it.
Observe what happens when you give the can a push force.

What happens

The can rolls away some distance, stops, and then comes back towards you as if by magic.

Background Information

Why it happens

As the can rolls away from you the weight inside the can winds up the elastic band. This causes energy to be stored up in the twisted bands in a direction opposite to the movement of the can. When this built up energy becomes great enough, the can stops rolling away, changes direction, and starts rolling back. This unwinds the bands again.

By the way

Watch out for sharp edges on the can, especially where you punch the holes in the lid and base.

1   2

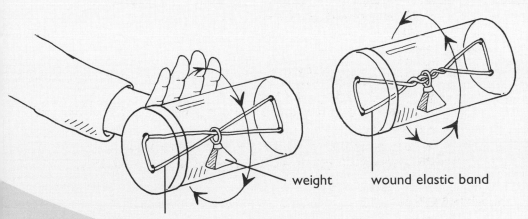

weight   wound elastic band

unwound elastic band

Curriculum links

KS2 Sc4 2d,e. QCA SoW 6E Forces in action
Envtl St/Science/E&F/CTE/Level E/Target 1

Trick your eyes

Spinning the card fast enough fools the eyes and puts the bird in the cage.

In the classroom

What you need

A piece of strong card, a pen and some string.

What you do

Draw a bird on one side of the card and a cage on the other.
Show the children both sides of your card.
Is it possible to get the bird in the cage?
Punch two holes on each side edge of the card.
Run strings through each pair of holes.
Wind up these strings between your hands.
Pull sharply to unwind them and ask the children to watch the card.

What happens

The card spins rapidly and the children see the bird in the cage.

Background Information

Why it happens

Our eyes retain impressions of light for a fraction of a second. The image of the cage, therefore, is retained on our retina and then the image of the bird joins it. This happens so fast that we are unable to distinguish between them. Our brain combines them and we see the bird in the cage.

By the way

This is how we see cartoon films at the cinema or on television. Providing we see 16 or more separate pictures each second, our eye will retain the image and we see the pictures move. Children can make their own whizzer with other ideas – perhaps a burglar behind bars or a fish in a fishbowl.

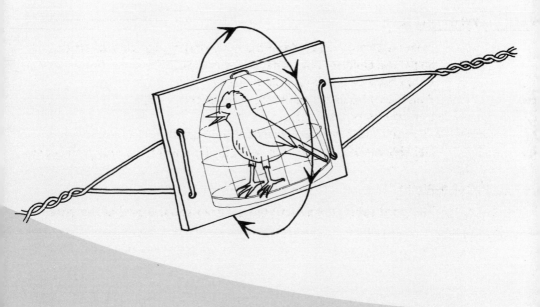

Curriculum links

KS2 Sc4 3d. QCA SoW 6F How we see things
Envtl St/Science/E&F/PUE/Level C/Target 2

What colour do you see?

Children investigate colour vision by tiring their eyes of one colour.

In the Classroom

What you need

A black pen, a green pen and a two large sheets of white paper.

What you do

Draw a simple face in black pen on one of the sheets of paper and give it green lips. Allow plenty of white space around the picture.
Ask the children to look at the picture for half a minute.
Tell them to relax their eyes as if they were soaking up the picture – which, in a way, they are.
Then tell them to look quickly at the blank sheet of white paper.
What colour are the lips now?

What happens

The children see an 'after image' of the face on the white paper with red (or at least pink) lips!

Background Information

Why it happens

The eye is full of little receptors, called *cones,* that see colour.
There are three kinds of cones: blue-sensitive cones to see blue,
red-sensitive cones to see red and yellow-sensitive cones to see
yellow. Green is made up of blue and yellow so blue-sensitive and
yellow-sensitive cones are used to see green. But after a while
these cones get tired, and when you look at a white sheet, only
the red-sensitive cones aren't tired – and you see red lips instead!
In other words, exposing a cone to too much of one colour (in
this case, green) makes it fire off so many impulses to the brain
that it needs time to recharge. During that period, the cones will
appear to be receiving red and will tell the brain so.

By the way

Some people have difficulty in seeing this effect. A few may have
colour vision deficiency, but this activity is not a test for colour
blindness. It is more likely that they don't understand what they
are looking for.
If you get red with green, what will you get with red, blue and yellow?
What about a blue square on a yellow background? Test it out.
Pictures painted in 'opposite' colours dazzle and seem to move.
Ask the children to try a painting using only bright red and green
paints.

green lips

Curriculum links

KS2 Sc4 3d. QCA SoW 6F How we see things
Envtl St/Science/E&F/PUE/Level C/Target 2

Find your blind spot

We all have a blind spot in our eyes as demonstrated by this activity.

In the Classroom

What you need

A piece of paper and a pen, per child.

What you do

Ask each child to draw a cross (left) and a spot (right) on a piece of paper, about 6 cm apart.
Tell them to cover their left eye with their hand, hold the paper at least 30 cm away, and look at the midpoint between the two.
They should then move the paper slowly towards their eyes.

What happens

As you bring the paper closer, at one optimum distance the spot disappears and the paper looks blank except for the cross. The spot reappears as the paper gets closer still.

Background Information

Why it happens

The image of the spot has fallen on the blind spot in their right eye. Everybody is familiar with the diagram of the inside of the eye, with the optic nerve leading off it. At this point where the nerve leads off, there are no light receptors – it is a blind spot – and light falling there cannot be interpreted. The brain covers up the gap by filling it in with what seems best – in this case, blank paper.

By the way

Do the activity again, but this time get the children to cover their right eye instead. The cross disappears.

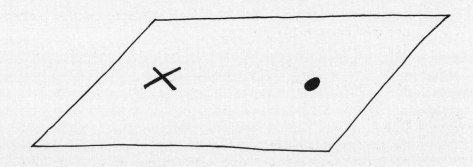

Curriculum links

KS2 Sc4 3d. QCA SoW 6F How we see things
Envtl St/Science/E&F/PUE/Level E/Target 4/Health Ed/TRH/PH/Level D/Target 4

unit 6F The sky in a jar

Adding a little milk to a jar of water allows you to demonstrate how light is scattered, giving the sky its colour.

In the classroom

What you need

A clear, straight-sided drinking glass or jar, water, milk, measuring spoons and a torch. This activity needs to be carried out in a darkened room.

What you do

Why is the sky blue?
Fill the glass or jar about two-thirds full of water.
Add one teaspoon (5 ml) of milk and stir.
Take the glass and torch into a darkened room.
First, hold the torch above the surface of the water and observe the water in the glass from the side.
Then, hold the torch to the side of the glass and look through the water directly at the light.
Finally, put the torch under the glass and look down into the water from the top.

What happens

When the torch is held above the surface of the water, the water should have a slight bluish tint. Then, when it is held at the side, the water should have a slightly reddish tint. Finally, when it is held under the glass, the water should have a deeper reddish tint.

44

Background Information

Why it happens

White light is made up of seven colours and has a blue end and a red end. The small particles of milk suspended in the water scattered the light from the torch in the same way that dust particles and molecules in the air scatter sunlight. Blue light has a shorter wavelength and is scattered more easily than the other colours. When the light shines in the top of the glass, the water looks blue because you see blue light scattered to the side. When you look through the water directly at the light, it appears red because most of the blue is removed by scattering.

By the way

When we look at a sunset on the horizon, we are looking through a far thicker slice of atmosphere than when we look straight up at the sun. As a result, there is more scattering, and the sky appears reddish. The same thing happens when air pollution is high and, as a result, the sky looks pink, i.e. smog.

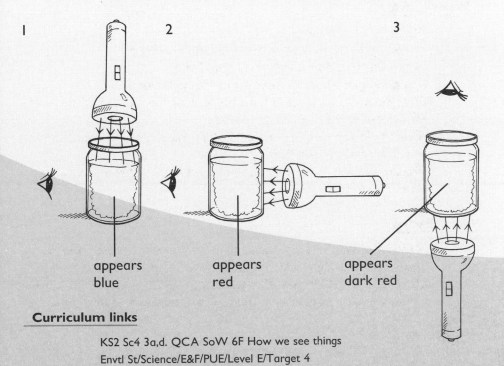

1

appears
blue

2

appears
red

3

appears
dark red

Curriculum links

KS2 Sc4 3a,d. QCA SoW 6F How we see things
Envtl St/Science/E&F/PUE/Level E/Target 4

45

Pass the power

Use a packet of sweets or a box of balls or quoits to illustrate how electricity flows round a circuit.

In the classroom

What you need

A packet of wrapped sweets (if you plan to let children eat them) or a box of balls. Quoits are even better. They are easy to manage and don't roll away if dropped.

What you do

First, get everyone to hold hands in a circle.
When you feel your hand squeezed, squeeze with your other hand.
Squeeze the hand of the child on one side of you.
The squeeze passes round the circle. Eventually it gets back to you. *Full circuit!*
Everyone in the circle holds a sweet or ball.
On your instruction, they pass them round the circle. This is like the flow of electricity.
You can ask some children to play the part of buzzers (the children hum) or motors (they turn round on the spot).
You then act as a switch and break the circuit of the sweets.

What happens

The original sweet (or squeeze) should return to the same person when the circuit is complete. When you act as a switch, you make a gap in the circuit to break the flow of sweets (or current).

Background Information

Why it happens

The sweets represent the electrons in a circuit. They are always there and it is the push of the battery (or the mains) that sends them round the circuit. On the way, they power buzzers, motors and lights. The circuit must be complete for the current to flow.

By the way

A battery is like a pump – pushing electrons round the circuit. The current is the same wherever you measure it. The more components in a circuit, the more the movement is resisted.

 Children who are permitted to eat sweets can eat the electrons at the end, but be aware of any food intolerances or diabetes.

Curriculum links

KS2 Sc4 1a. QCA SoW 6G Changing circuits
Envtl St/Science/E&F/PUE/Level C/Target 4

Scottish referencing key

Environmental Studies (Envtl St): Science	
ATTAINMENT OUTCOMES	SKILLS STRANDS
Earth and space (E&S)	Earth in space (ES) Materials from earth (ME) Changing materials (CM)
Energy and forces (E&F)	Properties and uses of energy (PUE) Conversion and transfer of energy (CTE) Forces and their effect (FTE)
Living things and the processes of life (LT&PL)	Variety and characteristic features (VCF) The processes of life (PL) Interaction of living things with their environment (ILTTE)
Health Education (Health Ed)	
ATTAINMENT OUTCOMES	SKILLS STRANDS
Taking responsibility for health (TRH)	Physical health (PH)